First Mental Arithmetic 2

Answers

Ann Montague-Smith

Schofield & Sims

Teacher's notes

The format of **First Mental Arithmetic** differs from that of traditional mental arithmetic materials in that the children read the questions themselves and write down their answers – as in the Key Stage 1 national tests. The individual books may be used flexibly and children may set their own pace. However, you might find it helpful to use one book per term.

The mathematical content of the **First Mental Arithmetic** activities should already have been covered in maths lessons and the reading content is kept simple. Nevertheless, you might consider asking a classroom assistant to work with a group of children, helping them to read the questions. Ask the assistant to note the names of children needing further help, and the activities or concepts that they find difficult. You can then provide the necessary teaching, support or additional practice.

Books 1 to 3

Each of the Year 1 books is split into two sections. If you are working through one book each term, you might aim to complete Section 1 (and possibly Check-up 1) just before the half-term break. Sections 1 and 2 are further divided into sessions. One double-page spread is provided for each session. Parts A, B and C of each session contain different question types; for further details, please see the back cover. Depending on the child's skills, a session's work may be completed during the course of a week or over whatever time span you feel is appropriate.

As children progress through the series, different levels of support are provided. In Books 1 to 3, the children have access to a horizontal number line, which is provided on every double-page spread. You may decide that the children would also benefit from using interlocking cubes or other counting equipment that helps them to work out some answers.

Encourage the children to use the following mental strategies when working through Book 2.

- For addition: counting on in ones from the larger number; they may find it helpful to keep a tally on their fingers.

- For subtraction (both 'take away' and 'difference'): counting up in ones from the smaller to the larger number; again, many children will find it helpful to keep a tally on their fingers.

Assessment

The Check-up Tests help you to monitor children's understanding.

- Check-ups 1 and 2 cover the concepts and skills of Sections 1 and 2 respectively.

- Check-up 3 covers all the number-based work in the book.

- Check-up 4, contained in the answers book only, is a photocopiable assessment covering measurement and geometry. Use it when all the other activities have been completed.

Record keeping

The photocopiable Group Record Sheets in this book allow you to note problem areas for particular children. For example, you might write *Counts objects to 12. Becomes confused beyond that...* Or, if a child still 'counts all' to add, you might write *Needs further experience in counting on in ones from the larger number.* Alternatively, you can simply record the child's marks. Use the completed sheets to plan appropriate work.

Contents

Section 1   Session 1

Session Focus
Counting up to 20 objects
Comparing and ordering numbers
Reading and writing numerals to 20

A

1 Count the spots. Write how many.

  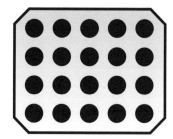

15   17   20

2 Write these numbers in order.

| **10** | **13** | **11** | **12** |

10   11   12   13

3 Write these numbers.

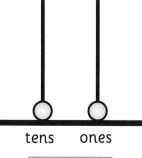 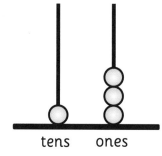 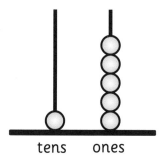

tens ones   tens ones   tens ones

| 1 | 1 | | 1 | 3 | | 1 | 5 |

B

4 Draw the number of dots.

   16      14

5 Write the missing numbers.

| **12** | **13** | 14 | 15 | 16 |

6 Draw beads to show these numbers.

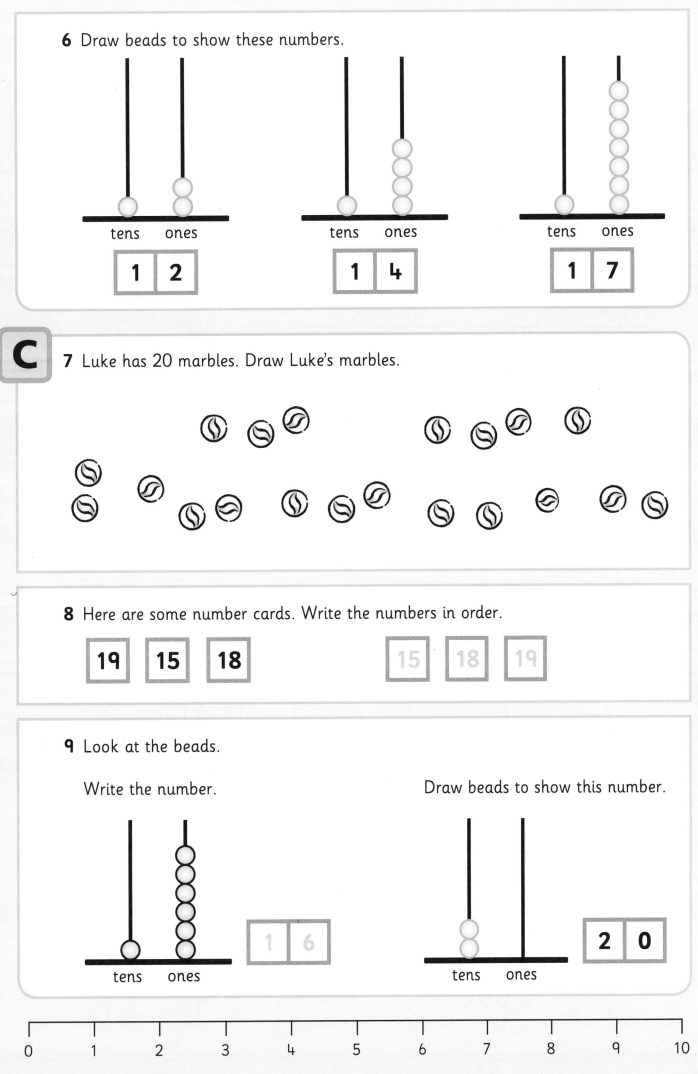

tens   ones
| 1 | 2 |

tens   ones
| 1 | 4 |

tens   ones
| 1 | 7 |

C

7 Luke has 20 marbles. Draw Luke's marbles.

8 Here are some number cards. Write the numbers in order.

| 19 | | 15 | | 18 |

| 15 | | 18 | | 19 |

9 Look at the beads.

Write the number.

| 1 | 6 |

Draw beads to show this number.

tens   ones

| 2 | 0 |

0   1   2   3   4   5   6   7   8   9   10

Section 1 Session 2

Session Focus
Adding by counting on, a ten and ones
1 more or 1 less
10 more or 10 less

A

1 Write the answers.

10 + 1 = 11   **10 + 3 =** 13   **10 + 5 =** 15

2 Write the missing numbers.

1 less   **1** more

3 Write the missing numbers.

10 less   **10** more

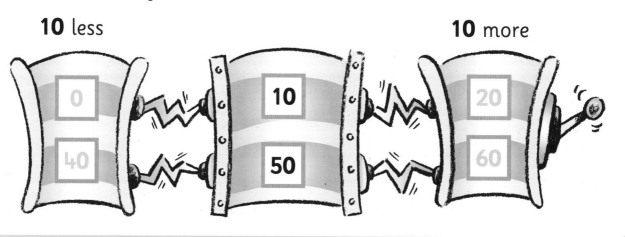

B

4 Write the missing numbers.

1 less   **1** more

5 Write the answers.

10 add **6** is ☐ 16

10 add **9** equals ☐ 19

10 add **7** is ☐ 17

10 and **10** makes ☐ 20

6 Write the missing numbers.

10 less

10 more

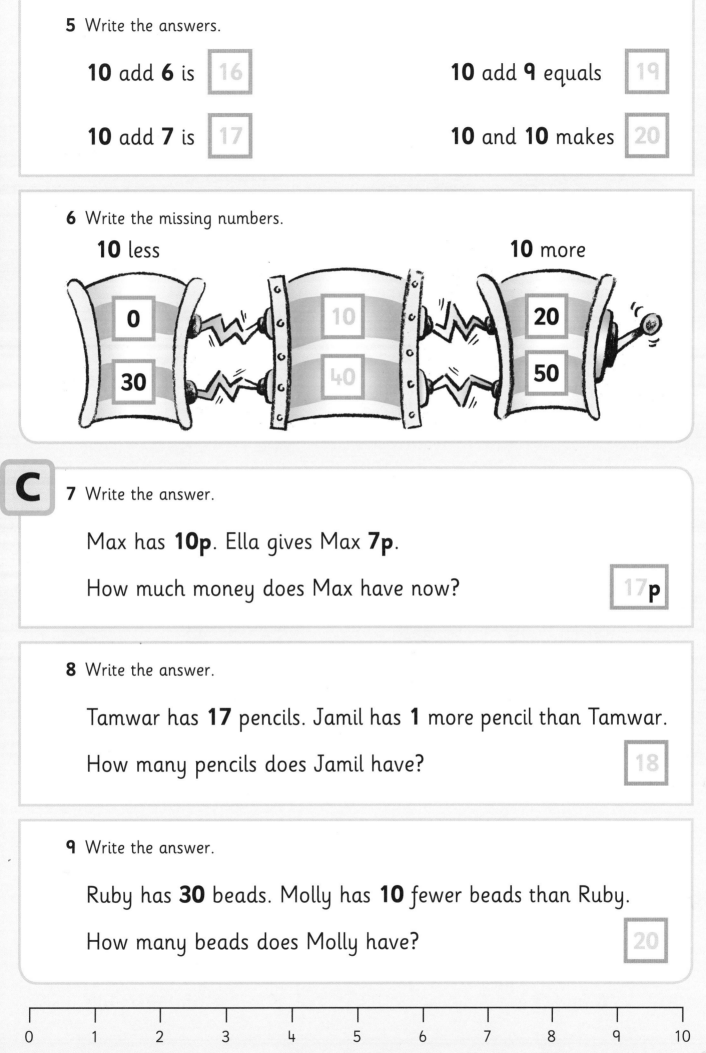

0

10

20

30

40

50

C

7 Write the answer.

Max has **10p**. Ella gives Max **7p**.

How much money does Max have now? ☐ 17 **p**

8 Write the answer.

Tamwar has **17** pencils. Jamil has **1** more pencil than Tamwar.

How many pencils does Jamil have? ☐ 18

9 Write the answer.

Ruby has **30** beads. Molly has **10** fewer beads than Ruby.

How many beads does Molly have? ☐ 20

0   1   2   3   4   5   6   7   8   9   10

Section 1   Session 3

Session Focus
Vocabulary of addition and subtraction
Subtracting by counting up from the smaller number
Visualising and naming common 2-D and 3-D shapes

A

1 Write the answers.

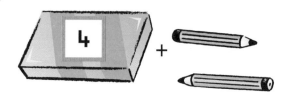   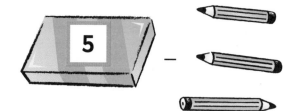

4 + 2 = 6   5 – 3 = 2

2 Count up from the smaller number. Write the answers.

4 – 3 = 1   6 – 4 = 2

3 Join the **2-D** shapes to their names.

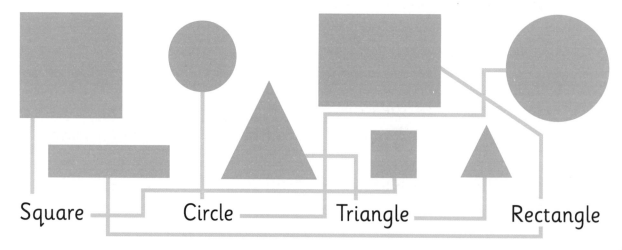

Square   Circle   Triangle   Rectangle

B

4 Write the answers.

5 add **2** is 7   **1** and **4** makes 5

6 and **3** is 9   **4** and **6** equals 10

5 Write the answers.

10 subtract **1** equals `9`

5 take away **3** leaves `2`

6 Join the **3-D** shapes to their names.

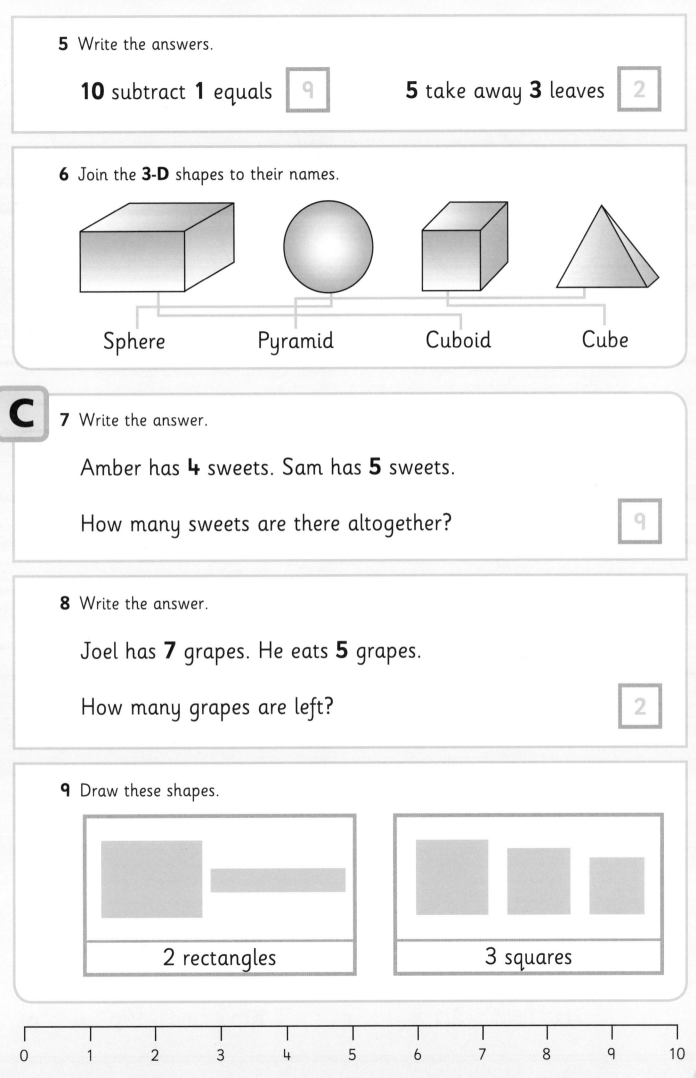

Sphere   Pyramid   Cuboid   Cube

C

7 Write the answer.

Amber has **4** sweets. Sam has **5** sweets.

How many sweets are there altogether? `9`

8 Write the answer.

Joel has **7** grapes. He eats **5** grapes.

How many grapes are left? `2`

9 Draw these shapes.

2 rectangles

3 squares

0 1 2 3 4 5 6 7 8 9 10

Section 1   Session 4

Session Focus
Counting totals
Doubles of numbers to 10
Pairs of numbers with a total of 10

A

1 Write how much money is in each purse.

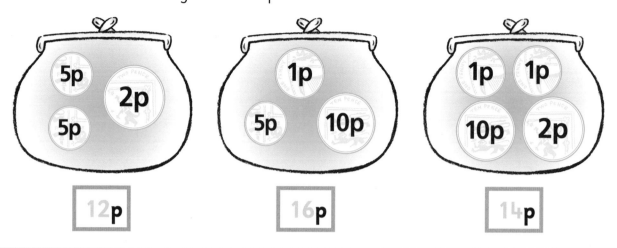

12 p   16 p   14 p

2 Write the doubles.

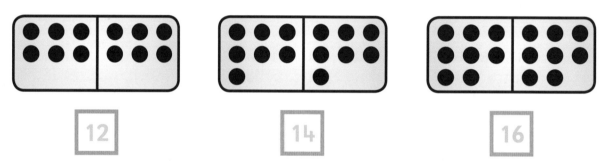

12   14   16

3 Write the answers.

$1 + 9 =$ 10 $2 + 8 =$ 10 $3 + 7 =$ 10

$4 + 6 =$ 10 $5 + 5 =$ 10 $6 + 4 =$ 10

$7 + 3 =$ 10 $8 + 2 =$ 10 $9 + 1 =$ 10

B

4 Write how much the coins total.

1p and 1p   2 p   5p and 5p   10 p

2p and 2p   4 p   10p and 10p   20 p

5 Write the answers.

$2 + 2 =$ ☐ 4 $8 + 8 =$ ☐ 16 $9 + 9 =$ ☐ 18

$10 + 10 =$ ☐ 20

6 Write the answers.

$5 +$ ☐ 5 $= 10$ $4 +$ ☐ 6 $= 10$ ☐ 7 $+ 3 = 10$

☐ 1 $+ 9 = 10$

C

7 Write the answer.

Jamie has **3** cookies. Noah has double that number.

How many cookies does Noah have?

8 Write the answer.

Grace has **7** peaches. Sunita has double that number.

How many peaches does Sunita have?

9 Write the answer.

Emma has **7** toffees. Leo has **3** toffees.

How many toffees is that in total?   ☐ 10

0   1   2   3   4   5   6   7   8   9   10

Section 1 Session 5

Session Focus
Measuring length by counting uniform non-standard units
Addition and subtraction facts for totals to 5
Pairs of numbers with a total of 10

A

1 Write the answer.

How many squares long is the line? 5

2 Write the answers.

$2 + 3 =$ 5 $\qquad$ $1 + 4 =$ 5 $\qquad$ $5 - 1 =$ 4

$3 + 2 =$ 5 $\qquad$ $5 - 0 =$ 5 $\qquad$ $4 - 2 =$ 2

$3 - 3 =$ 0 $\qquad$ $5 - 4 =$ 1

3 Write the answers.

$9 + 1 =$ 10 $\qquad$ $4 + 6 =$ 10 $\qquad$ $2 + 8 =$ 10

$7 + 3 =$ 10 $\qquad$ $0 + 10 =$ 10 $\qquad$ $5 + 5 =$ 10

$6 + 4 =$ 10 $\qquad$ $1 + 9 =$ 10 $\qquad$ $10 + 0 =$ 10

4 Draw the answer.

Draw a line that is **4** squares long.

B

5 Write the answers.

2 add **2** is equal to $\qquad$ **5** take away **3** equals 2

4 and **1** makes 5 $\qquad$ **4** take away **2** leaves

12

6 Write the answers.

$4 +$ 6 $= 10$ 3 $+ 7 = 10$ $9 + 1 =$ 10

2 add 8 makes **10**

7 Write the answer.

Some string is the same length as **8** pencils.

How many pencils long is half the string?   4

8 Write the answers.

5 cats are on the wall. **3** cats jump off.

How many cats are left on the wall?   2

4 cats sit on the grass. **1** more cat sits on the grass.

How many cats are there altogether?   5

9 Write the answer.

There are **6** books on the window sill.

There are **4** books on the table.

How many books is that in total?   10

```
0    1    2    3    4    5    6    7    8    9    10
```

Section 1 Check-up 1

Session Focus
Counting up to 20
Ordering numbers
Addition, Subtraction and 3-D shapes

1

1 Count the dots.

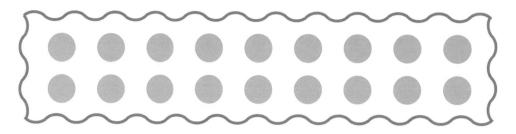

18

2 Write the numbers in order.

| 10 | 8 | 15 | 12 |

| 8 | 10 | 12 | 15 |

3 Write these numbers.

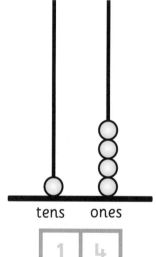

tens ones

| 1 | 4 |

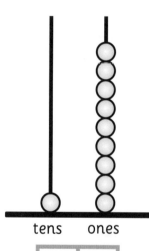

tens ones

| 1 | 9 |

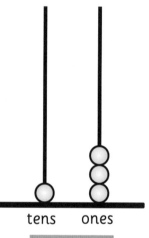

tens ones

| 1 | 3 |

4 Write the missing numbers.

5 + 5 = 10   9 + 1 = 10   6 + 4 = 10

5 Write the missing numbers.

1 less   **1** more   **10** less   **10** more

18 — **19** — 20   10 — **20** — 30

14

6 Write the missing numbers.

4 and $\boxed{6}$ makes **10**

7 add **3** equals $\boxed{10}$

10 minus $\boxed{8}$ equals **2**

$\boxed{5}$ add **5** makes **10**

7 Write the missing numbers.

$3 + \boxed{1} = 4$

$5 - \boxed{2} = 3$

$\boxed{2} + 2 = 4$

8 Write the answers.

$9 - 6 = \boxed{3}$

$8 - 6 = \boxed{2}$

$10 - 7 = \boxed{3}$

9 Write the names of these **3-D** shapes.

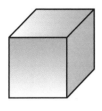 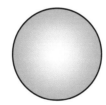 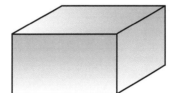 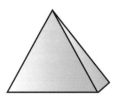

| Cube | Sphere | Cuboid | Pyramid |

10 Write the doubles.

6 $\boxed{12}$

7 $\boxed{14}$

9 $\boxed{18}$

11 Write the answer.

 How long is this line? $\boxed{6}$ squares

| 0 | 1 | 2 | 3 | 4 | 5 | 6 | 7 | 8 | 9 | 10 |

Section 2   Session 1

Session Focus
Adding by counting on
Subtracting by counting up from the smaller number
Ordering by weight and capacity

A

1 Write the totals.

$4 + 2 =$ 6 $6 + 2 =$ 8 $6 + 3 =$ 9

2 Write the answers.

$5 - 3 =$ 2 $7 - 3 =$ 4 $7 - 5 =$ 2

3 Tick the bag that is heavier.

B

4 Write the answers.

$3 + 4 =$ 7 $6 + 1 =$ 7 $4 + 5 =$ 9

$5 + 5 =$ 10 $2 + 5 =$ 7 $6 + 2 =$ 8

5 Write the answers.

$7 - 5 =$ 2 $8 - 4 =$ 4 $6 - 3 =$ 3

6 Tick the jar that has more.

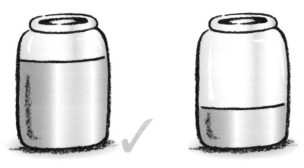

7 Write the answer.

Anil has **4** sweets. Katie has **3** sweets.

How many sweets do Anil and Katie have altogether?   7

8 Write the answer.

Oliver has **8** blueberries. He eats **3** blueberries.

How many blueberries does Oliver have left?   5

9 Tick the jar that is full. Circle the jar that is empty.

0	1	2	3	4	5	6	7	8	9	10

Section 2 Session 2

Session Focus
Ordering by weight and capacity
Telling the time to the hour
Addition and subtraction sentences

A

1 Tick the lighter one.

2 Write the time.

| 5 | o'clock | 10 | o'clock | 1 | o'clock |

3 Write the answers.

$$4 + \text{(marbles)} = 7$$

$$5 + \text{(socks)} = 10$$

$$9 - \text{(onions)} = 5$$

$$10 - \text{(blueberries)} = 3$$

B

4 Tick the jar with less.

5 Draw the hands to show the time.

 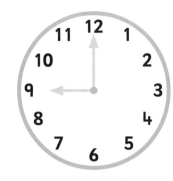 

7 o'clock   **9** o'clock   **3** o'clock

6 Write the answers.

$2 + \boxed{6} = 8$ $6 - \boxed{4} = 2$ $8 - \boxed{5} = 3$

C

7 Tick the jar that is holding least.

8 Write the answer.

Ella gets to school at **9** o'clock. She has lunch at **12** o'clock.

How long has she been at school? $\boxed{3}$ hours

9 Write the answer.

Kai has **10** marbles. He gives **3** marbles to Imogen.

How many marbles has Kai now?

| 0 | 1 | 2 | 3 | 4 | 5 | 6 | 7 | 8 | 9 | 10 |

Section 2 Session 3

Session Focus
Ordering by length
Addition and subtraction sentences
Position, direction and movement

1 Tick the longer one.

 ✓    ✓

2 Write the answers.

   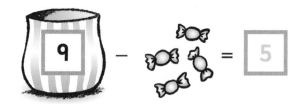

3 Draw a line to show how the cat can get to his basket.

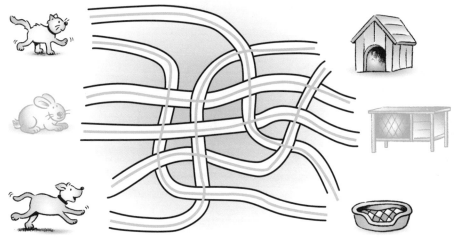

Only one line should be drawn for the dog.

4 Look at the picture in question 3.

Draw a rabbit between the cat and the dog.

Draw a hutch between the basket and kennel.

5 Tick the longest.

 ✓

6 Write the answers.

7 add **3** equals `10`   **2** and **4** is equal to `6`

5 subtract **3** leaves `2`   **7** minus **4** equals `3`

C

7 Write the answers.

Who is the taller? `Mum`

How much taller? `3` bricks

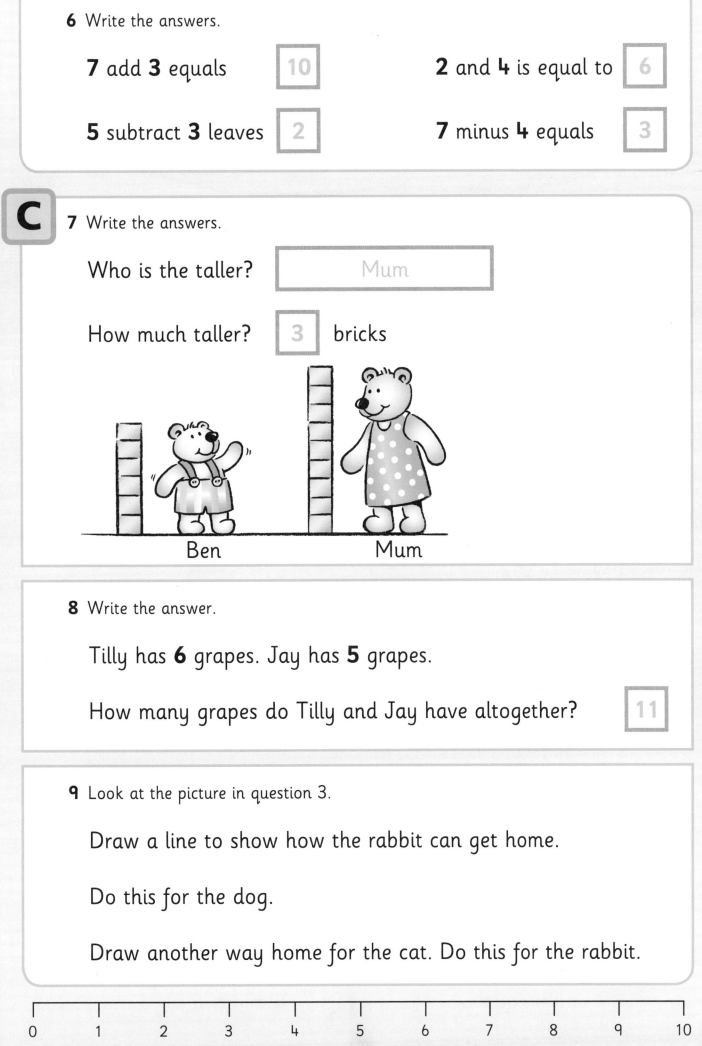

Ben   Mum

8 Write the answer.

Tilly has **6** grapes. Jay has **5** grapes.

How many grapes do Tilly and Jay have altogether? `11`

9 Look at the picture in question 3.

Draw a line to show how the rabbit can get home.

Do this for the dog.

Draw another way home for the cat. Do this for the rabbit.

0	1	2	3	4	5	6	7	8	9	10

Section 2 Session 4

Session Focus
Counting in 1s, 2s, 5s and 10s
Addition and subtraction sentences
Whole, half and quarter turns

1 Continue the pattern.

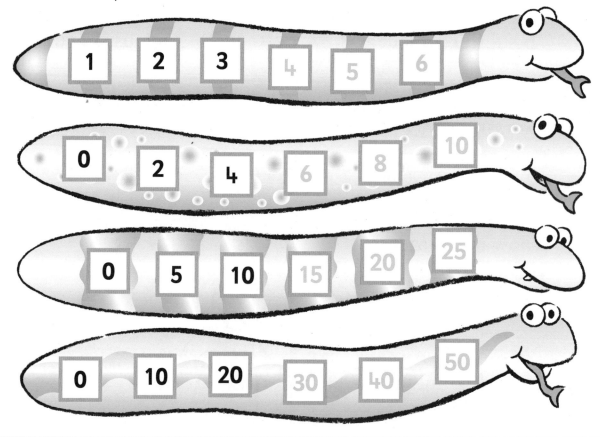

1   2   3   4   5   6

0   2   4   6   8   10

0   5   10   15   20   25

0   10   20   30   40   50

2 Write the answers.

+ 5 = 9   8 – = 1

3 Tick the teddy that has made half a turn.

   ✓

B

4 Write the answers.

7 add **4** equals 11   **6** minus **6** is 0

22

5 Write the missing numbers.

| 6 | 8 | 10 | 12 | 14 | 16 |

| 0 | 5 | 10 | 15 | 20 | 25 |

6 Tick the car that has made a quarter turn.

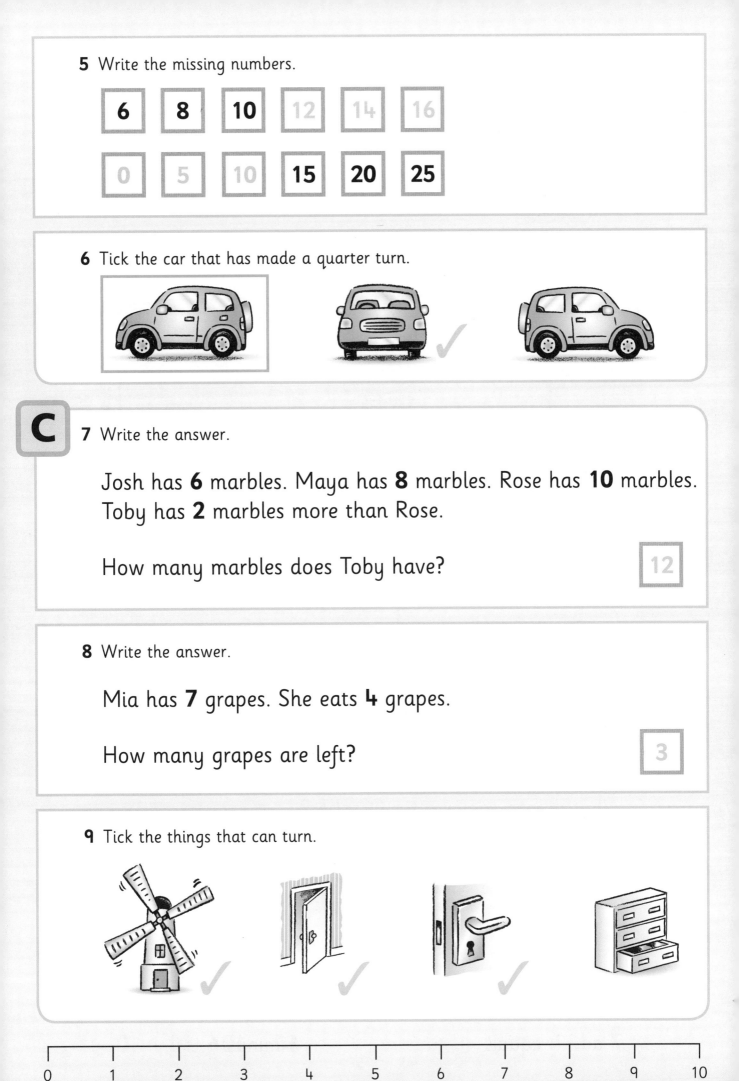

C

7 Write the answer.

Josh has **6** marbles. Maya has **8** marbles. Rose has **10** marbles.
Toby has **2** marbles more than Rose.

How many marbles does Toby have?   12

8 Write the answer.

Mia has **7** grapes. She eats **4** grapes.

How many grapes are left?   3

9 Tick the things that can turn.

0   1   2   3   4   5   6   7   8   9   10

Section 2   Session 5

Session Focus
Combining groups of 2, 5 or 10
Addition and subtraction sentences
Dates, months and years

A

1 Write the answers.

$2 + 2 + 2 =$ 6

$5 + 5 + 5 =$ 15

2 Write the answers.

$7 + 2 =$ 9

$3 + 6 =$ 9

$2 + 8 =$ 10

3 Write the answers.

$7 - 5 =$ 2 $9 - 6 =$ 3

B

4 Write the answers.

What month comes after May?

June

What month comes after October?

November

5 Use the number line to help you. Write the answers.

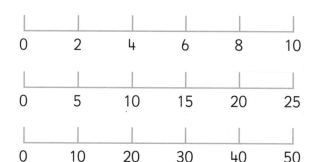

$2 + 2 + 2 + 2 =$ 8

$5 + 5 + 5 + 5 =$ 20

$10 + 10 + 10 + 10 =$ 40

6 Write the answers.

7 take away **4** leaves `3`   **8** subtract **6** equals `2`

4 minus **2** is equal to `2`   **7** subtract **2** equals `5`

6 take away **4** leaves `2`   **9** subtract **6** equals `3`

5 subtract **0** equals `5`   **10** take away **3** leaves `7`

9 minus **4** equals `5`   **4** subtract **4** leaves `0`

C

7 Write the answers.

Today's date is **1** January **2016**.
What date will it be tomorrow?

`2 January 2016`

Today's date is **13** September **2015**.
What date will it be tomorrow?

`14 September 2015`

---

8 Write the answer.

There are **4** red grapes and **5** green grapes on the plate.

How many grapes are there in total?   `9`

---

9 Write the answer.

There are **8** grapes on the plate. Eddie eats **7** grapes.

How many grapes are left?   `1`

```
0    1    2    3    4    5    6    7    8    9    10
```

Section 2 Session 6

Session Focus
Addition and subtraction sentences
Combining groups of 2, 5 or 10
Sharing into equal groups

A

1 Write the answers.

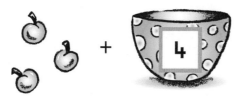   

$3 + 4 = \boxed{7}$ $9 - 8 = \boxed{1}$

2 Count along the number line. Write the answers.

| | | | | | | | | | | |
0 2 4 6 8 10 12 14 16 18 20

$2 + 2 + 2 + 2 + 2 + 2 = \boxed{12}$

| | | | | | | | |
0   5   10   15   20   25   30   35   40

$5 + 5 + 5 + 5 + 5 + 5 = \boxed{30}$

| | | | | | |
0   10   20   30   40   50   60

$10 + 10 + 10 + 10 + 10 = \boxed{50}$

3 Share the flowers between the vases. Write the answers.

6 shared by **2** is $\boxed{3}$ **10** shared by **5** is $\boxed{2}$

B

4 Write the answers.

7 add **2** is $\boxed{9}$ **9** minus **7** is $\boxed{2}$

5 Start at zero. Write the answers.

Make **3** jumps of **2** $\boxed{6}$ Make **3** jumps of **5** $\boxed{15}$

6 Use the pictures to help you. Write the answers.

Share **6** cubes between **2** plates.

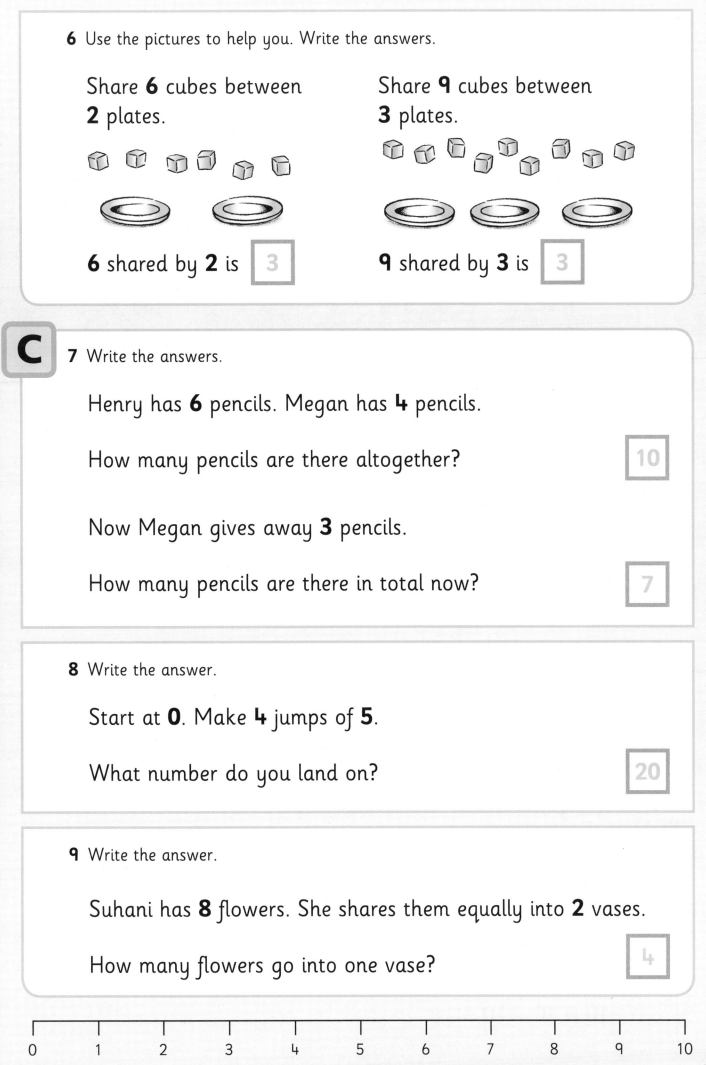

Share **9** cubes between **3** plates.

6 shared by **2** is ┃ 3 ┃

9 shared by **3** is ┃ 3 ┃

C

7 Write the answers.

Henry has **6** pencils. Megan has **4** pencils.

How many pencils are there altogether? ┃ 10 ┃

Now Megan gives away **3** pencils.

How many pencils are there in total now? ┃ 7 ┃

8 Write the answer.

Start at **0**. Make **4** jumps of **5**.

What number do you land on? ┃ 20 ┃

9 Write the answer.

Suhani has **8** flowers. She shares them equally into **2** vases.

How many flowers go into one vase? ┃ 4 ┃

0   1   2   3   4   5   6   7   8   9   10

Section 2 Check-up 2

Session Focus
Addition, Subtraction, Sharing into equal groups, Ordering by length, weight and capacity, Telling the time to the hour, Position, direction and movement

2

1 Write the answers.

$7 + 2 = \boxed{9}$ $\qquad$ $9 - 4 = \boxed{5}$

2 Tick the shortest tail.

3 Write the time.

$\boxed{8}$ o'clock

4 Write the answers.

$8 + 3 = \boxed{11}$ $\qquad$ $7 - 4 = \boxed{3}$

5 Write the answers.

$2 + 2 + 2 = \boxed{6}$ $\qquad$ $5 + 5 + 5 + 5 = \boxed{20}$

$10 + 10 + 10 = \boxed{30}$

6 Share these. Write the answers.

8 shared by **2** is | 4 |

12 shared by **3** is | 4 |

7 Draw a giraffe between the elephant and lion.

8 Complete the patterns.

| 6 | 7 | 8 | 9 | 10 | 11 |

| 2 | 4 | 6 | 8 | 10 | 12 |

| 0 | 10 | 20 | 30 | 40 | 50 |

9 Tick the dog that has made a half turn.

   ✓

0　1　2　3　4　5　6　7　8　9　10

Check-up 3   Number

3

1 Write the numbers in order.

| **13** | **16** | **15** | **14** |

| 13 | 14 | 15 | 16 |

2 Write the number.

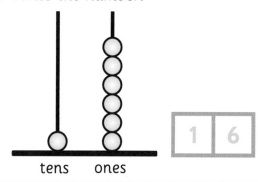

tens   ones

| 1 | 6 |

3 Write the answers.

$10 + 7 =$ 17 $10 + 10 =$ 20

4 Write the answers.

1 more than **10** is 11   **10** more than **20** is 30

5 Write the answers.

5 add **6** is 11   **9** minus **3** is 6

6 Count up from the smaller number to find the answers.

$8 - 3 =$ 5 $9 - 5 =$ 4

7 Write the answers.

$5 + 5 =$ 10 $9 + 9 =$ 18

8 Write the answers.

$1 + 9 = \boxed{10}$ $\qquad$ $2 + \boxed{8} = 10$

9 Write the answers.

$2 + 3 = \boxed{5}$ $\qquad$ $5 - 4 = \boxed{1}$

10 Count on from the larger number. Write the answers.

$3 + 4 = \boxed{7}$ $\qquad$ $2 + 5 = \boxed{7}$

11 Complete the patterns.

| 9 | 10 | 11 | 12 | 13 | 14 |

| 8 | 10 | 12 | 14 | 16 | 18 |

| 10 | 15 | 20 | 25 | 30 | 35 |

| 20 | 30 | 40 | 50 | 60 | 70 |

12 Write the answers.

$2 + 2 + 2 + 2 + 2 = \boxed{10}$ $\qquad$ $5 + 5 + 5 + 5 + 5 = \boxed{25}$

13 Share these cakes. Write how many on each plate.

15 shared by **3** is $\boxed{5}$

0 1 2 3 4 5 6 7 8 9 10

Check-up 4 Measurement and Geometry

1 Tick the heavier one.

2 Tick the jar that is full.

3 Tick the shortest one.

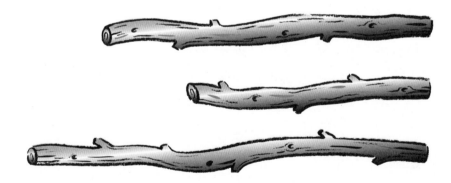

4 Write how long the ribbon is.

 squares long

Check-up 4 (page 2)

5 Write the time these clocks show.

⬜ o'clock   ⬜ o'clock   ⬜ o'clock

6 Draw these shapes.

Circle   Rectangle   Triangle   Square

7 Tick the cubes. Circle the pyramids.

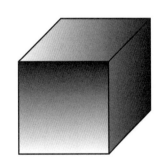
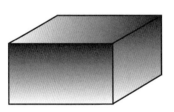

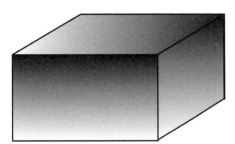

Check-up 4 (page 3)

8 Draw

a book on the table.

a cat under the table.

a chair next to the table.

9 Circle the quarter turn.

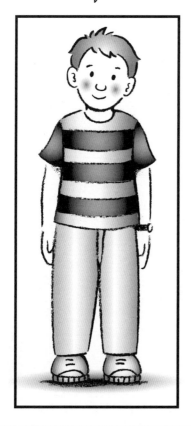  

Check-up 4 Answers
Measurement and Geometry

Session Focus
Order by length, weight and capacity
Telling the time to the hour
Shapes
Position and movement

1 Tick the heavier one.

2 Tick the jar that is full.

3 Tick the shortest one.

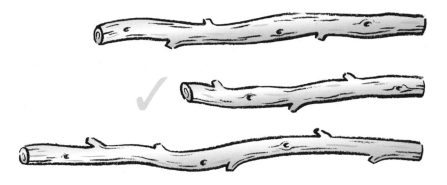

4 Write how long the ribbon is.

 squares long

35

5 Write the time these clocks show.

| 3 | o'clock | | 12 | o'clock | | 7 | o'clock |

6 Draw these shapes.

Circle   Rectangle   Triangle   Square

7 Tick the cubes. Circle the pyramids.

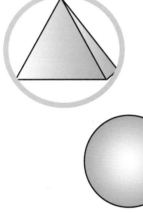 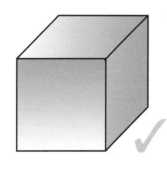 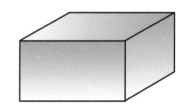

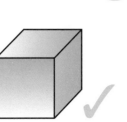 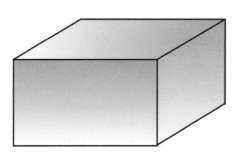 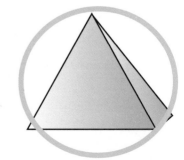

8 Draw

a book on the table.

a cat under the table.

a chair next to the table.

9 Circle the quarter turn.

Section 1   Group Record Sheet

Class _____

Name	Counting quantities up to 20	Comparing and ordering small numbers to 20	Reading, writing and ordering numbers to 20	Writing 1 more/ 1 less, 10 more/ 10 less numbers	Adding by counting on, a ten and ones	Vocabulary of addition and subtraction	Naming common 2-D and 3-D shapes	Subtracting by counting up	Totals of 10	Doubles of numbers to 10	Counting totals	Addition and subtraction facts for totals to 5	Measuring length by counting uniform non-standard units
	Session 1	Session 1	Session 1	Session 2	Session 2	Session 3	Session 3	Session 3	Session 4	Session 4	Session 4	Session 5	Session 5

Section 2 Group Record Sheet

Class _____

Name	Adding by counting on Session 1	Subtracting by counting up Session 1	Ordering by weight and capacity Session 1	Addition and subtraction sentences Session 2	Telling the time to the hour Session 2	Position, direction and movement Session 3	Counting in 1s, 2s, 5s, 10s Session 4	Whole, half and quarter turns Session 4	Combining groups of 2, 5 or 10 Session 5	Sharing into equal groups Session 6

Full list of Schofield & Sims First Mental Arithmetic books

Pupil books

First Mental Arithmetic 1	ISBN 978 07217 1163 8
First Mental Arithmetic 2	ISBN 978 07217 1164 5
First Mental Arithmetic 3	ISBN 978 07217 1165 2
First Mental Arithmetic 4	ISBN 978 07217 1166 9
First Mental Arithmetic 5	ISBN 978 07217 1167 6
First Mental Arithmetic 6	ISBN 978 07217 1168 3

Answer books

First Mental Arithmetic 1 Answers	ISBN 978 07217 1169 0
First Mental Arithmetic 2 Answers	ISBN 978 07217 1170 6
First Mental Arithmetic 3 Answers	ISBN 978 07217 1171 3
First Mental Arithmetic 4 Answers	ISBN 978 07217 1172 0
First Mental Arithmetic 5 Answers	ISBN 978 07217 1173 7
First Mental Arithmetic 6 Answers	ISBN 978 07217 1174 4

Teacher's Guide

First Mental Arithmetic Teacher's Guide	ISBN 978 07217 1210 9

Free downloads

A range of free downloads is available from the Schofield & Sims website (www.schofieldandsims.co.uk). These downloads may be used to support pupils in their learning, both in school and at home. They include the following items:

- two **First Mental Arithmetic** Entry Tests to help you choose the best book for each individual

- an Achievement Award certificate for each **First Mental Arithmetic** book

- Maths Facts downloads to provide a quick reference tool

- a National Curriculum Chart to show how each book supports the programmes of study.